Letterland

Phonics Practice 6

24 pages

Decodable text

Contains:
oi, oy, aw, au,
ou, ow (as in how),
air, ear, Ending -ed

✓ DfE Systematic Synthetic Phonics (SSP) validated

Name:

A boy called Roy

oy, oi as in boy, coin

1. Roy is leaping into words. Read the words, then join each word to the matching picture. Write the words again.

toys   •   •    toys

boys   •   •    _____

soy   •   •    _____

boil   •   •    _____

coins •   •    _____

point •   •    _____

toilet •   •   _____

2. Cross out the word that does not make sense in the sentence. Trace over the one that does.

She put an egg in the pan to boil / ~~boy~~.

The boy's toy / ~~toil~~ box is full.

I need to go to the ~~boil~~ / toilet.

3. Read the sentences, and write the sentence under the picture that matches. Cross out the sentence that does not match a picture.

Roy will enjoy his new toy.

Let's avoid those boys.

The robot toy can pick up coins.

Annie Apple and Walter Walrus   **aw, au** as in saw, cause

1. Colour in Annie Apple and Walter Walrus. Then write **aw** on the lines. Read the words and match them to the pictures.

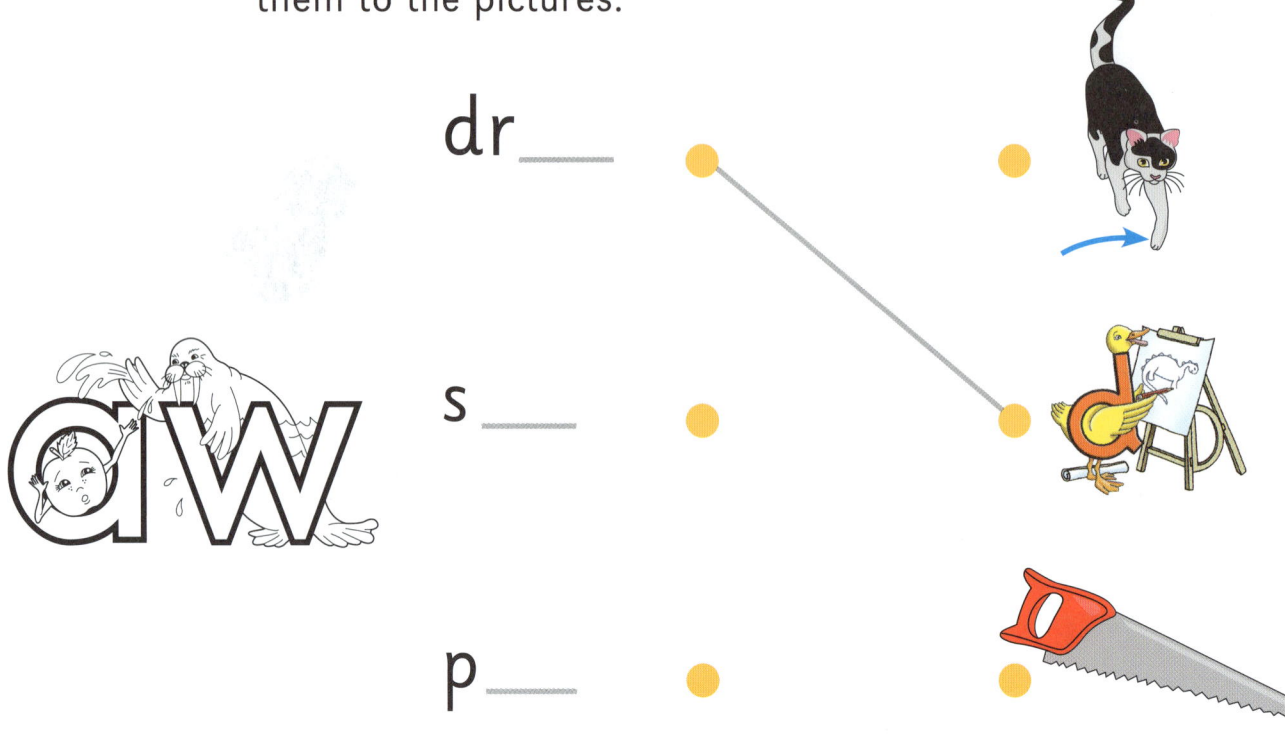

dr___

s___

p___

2. Read the two words beneath each picture. Circle the word that matches the picture.

straw   stove   hawk   haul   lawn   yawn

jigsaw   saw   jar   jaw   door   dawn

3. Write a word for each picture below.

   launch   saucer

   A cup and _____ .

   A rocket _____ .

4. Label this autumn scene with the **aw** and **au** words below.

saucer   paw   saw   yawn   straw   jigsaw

Review - aw, au, ew

1. Read the sentences. Then colour the star next to the matching picture.

This jigsaw has paw prints on it.

He did not use a straw to drink his strawberry milk.

The astronaut is an author.

They applaud the new show.

2. Read the sentence. Then write a new sentence using some of the other words.

| I | a | saw | yawn | man | cat | paw | got | jigsaw | straw |

I saw a man yawn.

3. Underline all the **aw**, **au** and **ew** words in the instructions below. Then complete the picture.

Draw claws on the cat's paws.
Draw a shrew escaping the cat.
Then draw a rocket launch in the sky.

4. Underline all the **aw**, **au** words in the story. Read it to a friend.

We went to see a rocket launch. We had to wait a long time so we did a jigsaw. We yawned, and then fell asleep.

When we woke up the rocket had launched!
Aw! That's awful!

 Oscar Orange and Walter Walrus **ow, ou** as in how, out

1. Colour in Oscar Orange and Walter Walrus. Write **ow** or **ou** on the lines. Read the words and match them to the pictures.

___l •   •

c___s •   •

br___n •   •

h___se •   •

cl___d •   •

r___nd •   •

2. Add **er** to each word, and write it under the picture.

show ⟶
flow ⟶ **er**
tow ⟶

  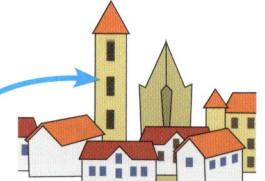

3. Label this town scene with the **ow** and **ou** words below.

| mountain | clowns | flowers | fountain |
| mouse | cow | ground | clouds |

4. Write the word for each picture. Then write the rhyming word below.

mountain   vowels   house
mouse   towels   fountain

 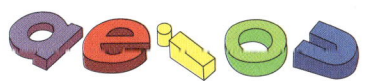 

_____   _____   _____

_____   _____   _____

Robots capturing Vowel Men

air as in fair

1. Link **air** to the words that contain their sound. Write the words in the spaces. Cross out the other pictures.

fair

2. Read the sentences, and write a word in each space.

| fairy chair upstairs downstairs hair |

A _____ with fair _____ flew _____. She jumped on a _____ and then on the bed. She then flew _____.

3. Read the sentences, and write a word in each space.

| fair   fairy   chair   hair   stairs |

I will dry my _____, then go to the _____.

The _____ is on the _____.

This pair are sitting on a _____.

Nick is pulling Golden Girl's _____.

Colour the picture!

 Robots capturing Vowel Men **ear** as in year and bear

Look at the words below where the robot is saying, "I can't hear!"

 ear  year

1. Write these **ear** words under the matching pictures.

spear   hear   beard   tears   fear   clear

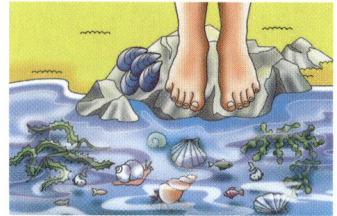   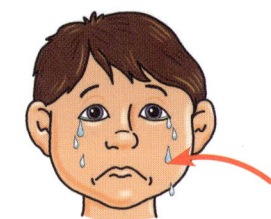   

clear   _____   _____

_____   _____   _____

2. Write these words besides their opposites.

appear   fearful   rear   cloudy   near

far _____   front _____

clear _____

brave _____   disappear _____

3. Sometimes we hear a different **ear** sound. The robot puffs out 'air'. Join these words to the matching pictures.

bear

pear

tear

Draw lines to join the pictures to the words, then to the story.

hear

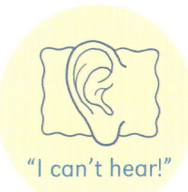
"I can't hear!"

pear

Puffing out air.

4. Read the sentences, and write a word in each space.

| bear   pear   ears   hear |

The _____ has picked

a _____.

I use my _____ to _____.

13

ed as in skated, smiled, hoped

1. Read the words. Say each with the -**ed** ending and listen to the sound it makes. Join it to the correct picture.

skate  skated •

wade _____ •

dive _____ •

smile  _____ •

rake _____ •

chase  _____ •

2. Read the words. Listen to the sound made by the **ed** ending. Write it under the Picture Coded **ed** with the same sound.

closed traded hated baked timed wiped
faded saved liked hoped piled skated

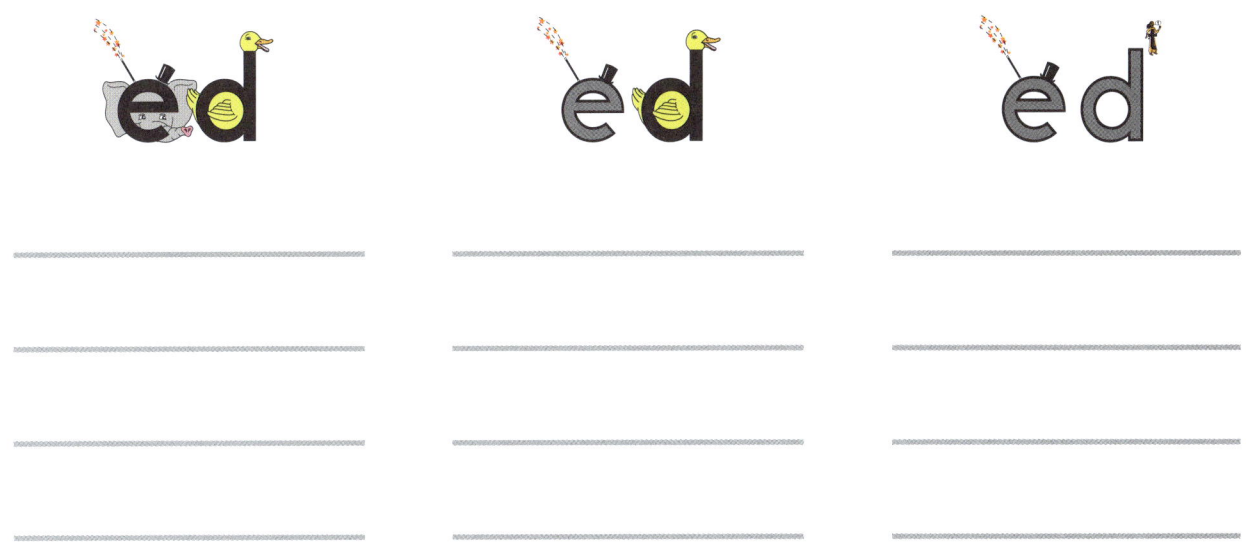

3. Cross out the word that does not make sense in the sentence. Trace over the one that does.

Max ~~skate~~ / skated until six o'clock.

Tess waved / ~~waves~~ at Harry as he hops by.

I hope that the shop is not ~~closes~~ / closed.

Rose ~~bake~~ / baked a cake.

Best friends to the rescue

Double consonants

Bouncy Barbara   Diana Duck   Golden Granny   Linda Lamp Light   Patsy Puppy   Talking Tom

1. Add the best friend and the suffix **ed** to each word. Read this story out loud to a partner.

The cat's cup is spot<u>ted</u>.

The cup tip____ up.

Her milk spilled.

The Hat Man grab____ a cloth.

He rub____ the milk off.

The cat and Hat Man hug____.

Then he hop____ off.

2. The words in blue are misspelled. Rewrite the sentences adding the Letterland best friends. Then read your sentences to a partner.

He hummed as he filled up the sink.

She spotted the ball and batted it.

The hawk flapped its wings.

She clapped her hands. Well done!

Review sounds and spelling patterns

1. Read the two words below each picture. Circle the word that matches the picture.

paint point   hook hawk   tower towel

 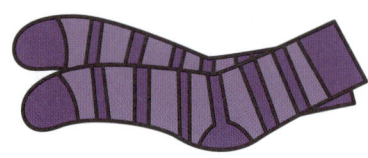 

hood hard   pair pour   shrew chew

new chew   pill pull   horse house

news nose   crown count   bear beard

fair faint   vowels vows   boy toy

2. Read and match the words to who said them. Copy the words in the correct place.

"I'll make a new roof that looks like that."

"These things in my cookbook look good."

"Mmm, I like to chew and munch melons."

Review sounds and spelling patterns

1. Read the story on your own. Then read it again out loud.

2. Look at the words in the box. Find the words in the story and make sure you have read them correctly.

A boy went out in the woods to crunch about in the yellow and brown leaves. Then he looked down and saw some gold coins on the ground. He crouched down and picked them up. Wow! He put them in his pocket. Then a loud growling sound made him jump. What was it? Was it a tiger lurking behind a tree? He ran back to his house.

"What was that sound?" he shouted.

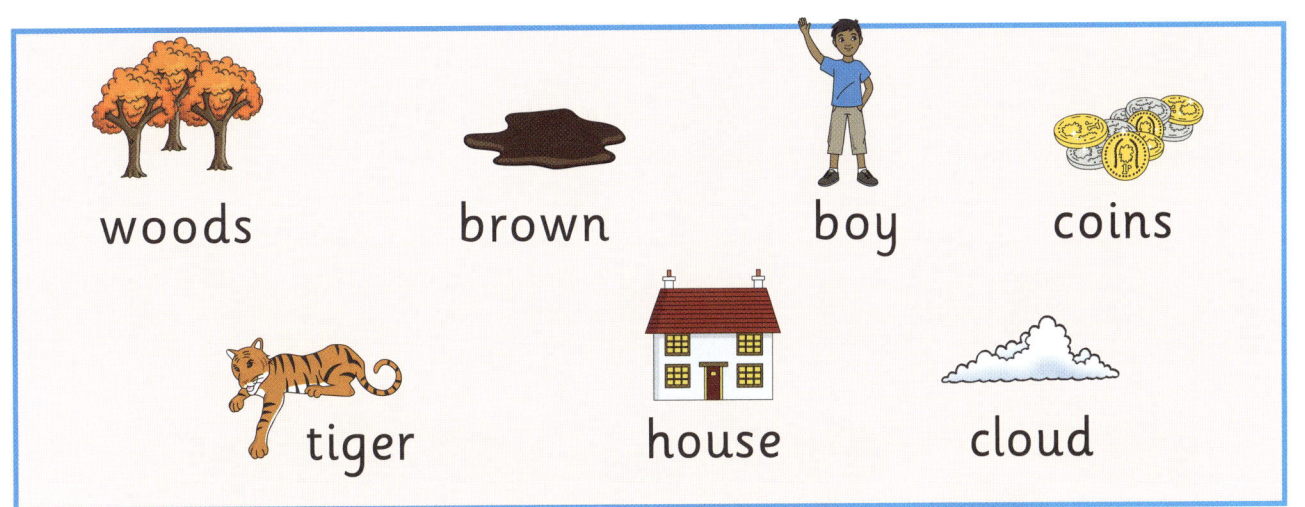

"Oh! I'm glad you came back to the house. Look at that cloud! That's a thunder cloud," said Mum.

"I'm glad it was not a tiger growling!" said the boy.

His mum smiled. "Tigers do not hide in clouds or in those woods!"

"Look what I did find in the woods! These fantastic gold coins!"

Review sounds and spelling patterns

1. Look at the pictures. Use some of the words in the box below each picture to write about what you see.

stay   away   holiday   play   clay

three   sheep   green   bee   tree

mouse house frown shout gown

Roy toy boy annoyed enjoys

yawn shawl awful paw thaw

How to use this book

On each page, read the instructions to the children. Discuss the pictures, as needed. Let them try and read all the words in the exercises themselves, as they are decodable.

Further vowel sounds and spellings
The workbooks are designed to consolidate and extend the teaching content of the Letterland *Phonics Teacher's Guide*. By the end of this workbook, they will have all the essential phonic information they need to understand how predictable many aspects of the English language are – and their reading vocabulary will be expanding exponentially!

Skills covered include:
- phonemic awareness
- decoding skills
- word building
- reading for meaning
- sentence completion
- using words in context when writing
- open-ended sentence writing.

It is important to use this workbook:
- when children are not tired
- when there are no background distractions
- for short periods of time
- with plenty of praise and encouragement.

Correct handwriting positions

Left-hander   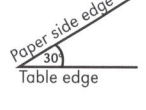   Right-hander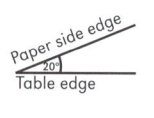

Fingertips 4cm from tip of pencil   Elbows off the table / Feet on floor   Chair slightly tilted / Feet on floor   Fingertips 2cm from tip of pencil

---

Published by Letterland International Ltd.
8/10 South Street, Epsom, Surrey, KT18 7PF, UK
© Letterland International 2021
10 9 8 7 6 5 4 3 2

ISBN: 978-1-78248-556-8
Product Code: TP70

LETTERLAND™ is a trademark of Letterland International Ltd.
Printed in China.

All rights reserved. No part of this publication may be reproduced, stored in a retrieval system, or transmitted in any form or by any means, electronic, mechanical, photocopying, recording or otherwise, without the prior permission of the Publisher or a licence permitting restricted copying in the United Kingdom issued by the Copyright Licensing Agency Ltd, 90 Tottenham Court Road, London W1P 0LP. British Library Cataloguing in Publication Data. A catalogue record for this book is available from the British Library.

Sassoon Infant is a typeface designed for children learning to read and write.
© Adrian Williams Design Ltd

Written and designed by Lisa Holt
Consultant: Lyn Wendon, originator of Letterland

You may also like:

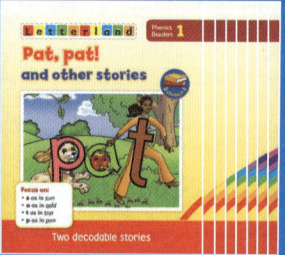 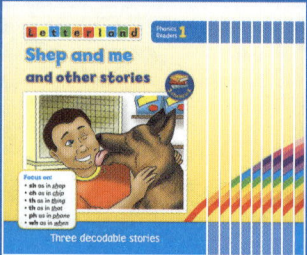

See our full range at: www.letterland.com

Please Note: These practice books match the teaching order in the Letterland *Phonics Teacher's Guide*.

For those who wish to follow a different teaching order the practice books can be used flexibly.

Code: TP70
ISBN 978-1-78248-556-8
9 781782 485568
Letterland Child-friendly phonics